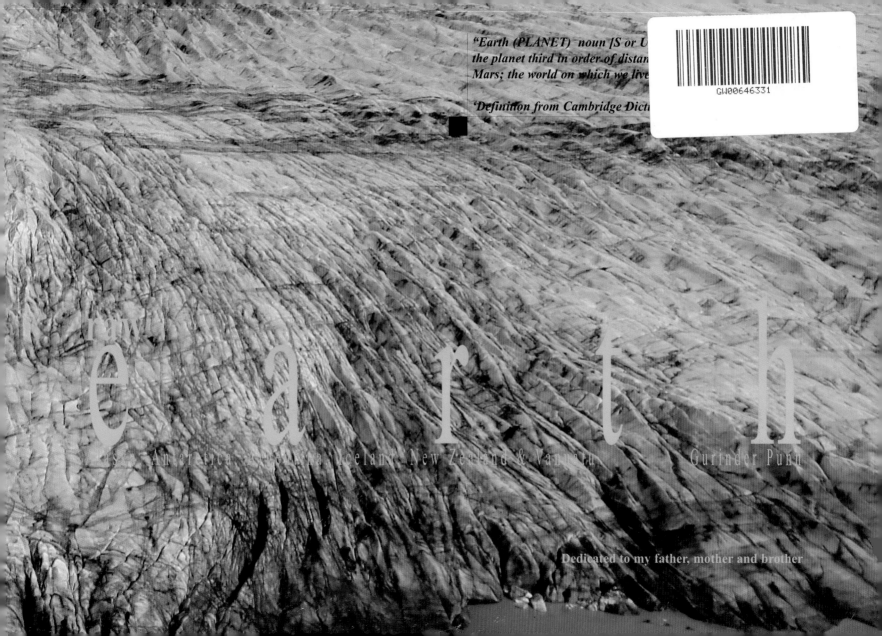

earth

Antarctica · Australia · Iceland · New Zealand & Vanuatu   Gurinder Punn

Dedicated to my father, mother and brother

raw

e a r t h

Alaska, Antarctica, Argentina, Iceland, New Zealand & Vanuatu

Gurinder Punn

Matador
9 De Montfort Mews
Leicester LE1 7FW. UK
Email: books@troubador.co.uk
Web: www.troubador.co.uk/matador
Tel: (+44) 116 255 9312

ISBN 10: 1-905886-24-1
ISBN 13: 978 1905886 241

Acknowledgements:
Jill Fardon for her tireless research, proof reading and support

Front cover: The Godley River in Aoraki/Mt Cook National Park, New Zealand
Inside cover: Skaftafelljokull, Iceland

Printed in the UK by The Cromwell Press Ltd, Trowbridge, Wilts, UK

Matador is an imprint of Troubador Publishing Ltd

raw earth

Alaska, Antarctica, Argentina, Iceland, New Zealand & Vanuatu

Contents

This book is a collection of photographs of my visits to some of the most beautiful, dramatic, fascinating and geologically active places in the world. It is not an exhaustive collection by any means, but I believe that the images and the accompanying narrative capture some of the most wonderful aspects of planet Earth. As a lay person I have been fascinated by the intricate workings of our planet for many years and this led me to read significant amounts of literature about our Earth and its place in the cosmos. My love of photography and my thirst for a better understanding of how our world works have been my motivation for writing this book.

The locations that are covered in this book are Alaska, Antarctica, Argentina, Iceland, New Zealand and Vanuatu. Each has its own fascinating story to tell about its formation and subsequent transformation into the beautiful landscape that we see today. I have divided the book into four chapters; Terra Firma, Glacialis, Aqua and Inferno and then extracted the salient features of each location to allow a visual comparative to be drawn by the reader. Thus, for example, the reader will be able to see glaciers from Alaska,

Argentina, Antarctica, Iceland and New Zealand all together in one section. A short but concise geological history of some of the main locations is also included but the reader is directed to the reference section for further reading. Throughout the book I have made references to the timescales involved in the formation of the featured locations, but it is worth putting these into context with the timescales for the formation of the Earth and indeed the Universe.

The very latest scientific theories tell us that the Universe is around 13700 million years old and that our planet is around 4560 million years old. We, as a Hominid species, have existed for no more than 7 million years, equivalent to about 0.05% of the age of the Universe or around 0.15% of the history of our planet. We only started to develop an understanding of our physical environment about 5000 years ago. It is only in the last 500 years, with the advent of the Copernican revolution that we have begun to adopt a rational and scientific approach to understanding our universe and our place in it. Put another way, if the age of the Earth was represented by a 24 hour clock, Hominids arrive on the

scene around 2 minutes to midnight, we start understanding our world at 0.09 seconds to midnight and the scientific renaissance only starts at 0.009 seconds to midnight!

Plate tectonics features repeatedly as it is such a fundamental process on our planet and is used to explain, among other things, mountain building. The significance of the ice cores drilled in Antarctica and other regions is also discussed and their importance in understanding past climate change is considered. The global significance of water and its role in the evolution of life and human civilization is also considered. The question of volcanism is discussed and explained with reference to fundamental geophysical processes going on deep within the Earth's core.

I have tried to give simple interpretations of the most current theories about the geophysical processes that mould and shape our planet. I have done so without going into too much technical detail because this is first and foremost a visual representation of some of our planet's most amazing and spectacular landscapes.

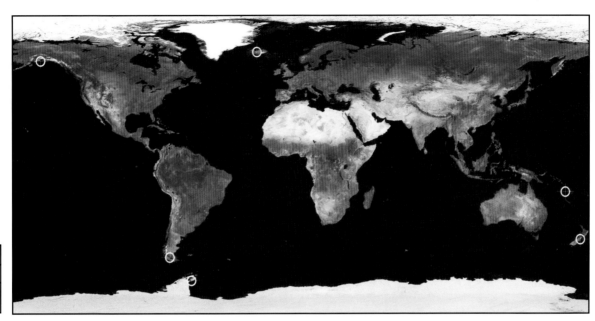

Argentina Main Locations

Place	Latitude	Longitude
Perito Moreno Glacier	50°29`S	73°03`W

Vanuatu Main Locations

Place	Latitude	Longitude
Mt Yasur	18°48`S	169°02`E

Wrangell National Pk, Alaska USA, Main Locations

Place	Latitude	Longitude
Bagley Icefields	60°03`N	141°02`W
Gates Glacier	60°52`N	141°51`W
Iceberg Lake	60°16`N	141°37`W
Long Glacier	60°49`N	142°06`W
Mt. Logan (Canada)	60°34`N	140°24`W
Mt. St. Elias	60°15`N	140°52`W
Root Glacier	60°47`N	141°59`W
Wrangell Mountains	60°27`N	141°49`W
Wrangell National Park	60°-62°30`N	141°-145°W

Antarctic Peninsula Main Locations

Place	Latitude	Longitude
Most Northerly Point	60°13`S	62°47`W
Most Southerly Point	65°53`S	62°52`W
Gerlache Straits	65°16`S	61°36`W
Graham Passage	65°16`S	61°36`W
Cuverville Island	64°41`S	62°38`W
Paradise Bay	64°53`S	62°53`W
Lemaire Channel	65°05`S	63°58`W
Vernadskiy Research Base	65°15`S	64°45`W
Trinity Island	63°50`S	60°44`W

Iceland Main Locations

Place	Latitude	Longitude
Drangey	65°56`N	19°40`W
Eyjafjallajökull/Tin-dfjallajökull region	63°55`N	19°09`W
Geysir/Strokkur	64°16`N	20°21`W
Haifoss	64°11`N	19°37`W
Lakagigar	64°02`N	17°54`W
Landmannalugar	64°02`N	19°07`W
Pingvellir National Park	64°16`N	17°54`W
Skeiðarársandur	63°51`N	17°05`W
Vatnajökull Ice cap region	64°25`N	16°55`W

New Zealand Main Locations

Place	Latitude	Longitude
Fox Glacier	43°39`S	169°59`E
Franz J Glacier	43°35`S	170°02`E
Lake Tekapo	43°53`S	170°31`E
Lake Wanaka	44°33`S	169°07`E
Milford Sound	44°40`S	167°54`E
Mt Aspiring	44°23`S	168°46`E
Aoraki/Mt Cook	43°36`S	169°59`E
Mt Tutoko	43°39`S	170°10`E
Queenstown	44°51`S	168°21`E

Terra Firma

What exactly are mountains and why are they located where they are on the globe? Furthermore, when we look at a mountain, the last thing we would imagine is that this huge lump of rock could actually be rising or falling on a daily basis. But that is exactly what is happening. We simply don't see it because the average rate of change is about 1 cm per year. The thing to remember is that over 1000 years is equivalent to about 100m up or down or nearly twice the height of Nelsons Column. Over a million years these rocks could rise or fall 10000m; but that's not what we see. None of the world's mountain ranges are that high. So what's going on?

The Earth's crust is made up of at least 13 huge slabs of rock; basaltic (as in the case of oceanic crust) and granitic (as in the case of continental crust). The thickness of continental crust is at the most 50km and oceanic crust is about 10km thick. All this literally floats upon the next layer down (called the lithosphere) which in turn sits above a region called the asthenosphere. These collectively are known as tectonic plates and are part of the uppermost mantle. All of the above layers in turn sit on the remainder of the mantle, with the core at the centre. The core is further divided into the outer liquid iron core and what is believed to be a single huge crystal of solid iron at the center. The distance from crust to core (the radius) is 6370km which means that the crust we live upon represents only about 0.5% of the thickness of the Earth. And yet so much geological activity seems to happen out here!

So how do mountains form? The important thing to remember about the oceanic and continental crust is that the former is heavier than the latter and as basic physics tells us, heavier materials will sink below lighter materials. But when two plates that are both continental crust happen to meet something else happens. As neither can sink below the other, a collision occurs forcing an uplifting of huge areas of continental crust. The result of this gargantuan collision is a mountain range.

Geologists call such a phase an orogeny. All the world's mountain ranges have been created in this way.

Left on their own, the mountains borne out of these collisions should simply keep rising or stay at their highest once the collisions of the crusts have ended. But let us not forget another basic law of physics; what goes up must come down and mountains are no exception to this universal principle. When the force that pushes them up subsides, gravity takes over and literally brings them down to earth again, albeit in a few million years. Another mountain killer is erosion and as we shall see with the Southern Alps in New Zealand, wind, rain and ice all play their part in the merciless destruction of these awesome wonders.

On some mountain ranges in the world, climbers have found seashells or fossils of creatures that obviously once had an aquatic lifestyle. This raises the question of how such marine creatures found themselves stranded up a mountain? The answer, it turns out, is that the rocks that make up the mountain range were once seafloor and that as the creatures died, they settled and became fossilized. As global sea levels fell the seafloor became exposed as land, and with the action of plate tectonics, was uplifted to form a mountain range. The Himalayas, the Southern Alps in New Zealand and many other ranges all started life at the bottom of the sea.

So perhaps the term 'rock solid' should be used with a little caution for even mountains are not as hard as they seem and it is amazing to think that the great ranges we see today will one day return to the ground from whence they were born.

The images on the following pages show the beauty of the Southern Alps, the breathtaking splendour of the Wrangell Range in Alaska and the colourful Landmannalugar range in Iceland.

South Island, New Zealand

This satellite image shows the location of the Southern Alps as a chain of mountains stretching from Nelson Lakes National Park in the north for some 500km to Mt Aspiring National Park in the South. All the images of New Zealand mountains shown here are from along this 500km stretch of land.

The oceanic part of the Australian plate is being subducted below the continental portion of the Pacific plate, upon which the South Island sits. This causes tremendous forces to push up rocks from depths of about 40km all along the Alpine fault and its tributaries.

There have been no less that 3 episodes of mountain building over the last 300 million years in this region and nowhere else do mountains rise and fall as rapidly as they do here. The geological evidence from sedimentary rocks, magnetization patterns around areas of sea floor spreading and isotopic dating, tell the story of how these mountains have risen and fallen repeatedly around 250, 105 and then 25 million years ago. The last phase which started about 25 million years ago is still one of mountain building and at a rate of about 3-4cm each year. The tectonic activity associated with this has also resulted in New Zealand taking on the familiar shape that we see today. Were it not for erosion by wind, water and ice, today's Southern Alps would extend some 20km into the stratosphere. However, the material of these mountains (Torlesse sand-stone and Hasst Schist) is being eroded away as fast as it is being uplifted by the tectonic activity.

The Alpine fault literally cuts through the South Island, entering land on the southwest coast at Milford Sound and running in a north-easterly direction until finally leaving land at KaiKoura on the east coast. As it does so the continental shelf plunges steeply down to 1000m causing an abyss close to the coast. It has been found that migrating whales use this region as a feeding ground.

Aoraki/Mt Cook (3755m) on the right with the Tasman Glacier directly below. On 14ᵗʰ Dec 1991 a rock avalanche occurred which travelled down the slopes at speeds of over 300kmph and carried with it over 14 million cubic metres of rock. It had the effect of lowering New Zealand's highest peak by around 10m within a few moments

A wide angle view of the Mt Cook Range and the cloud covered valley hiding the mighty Tasman Glacier

The majestic and near pyramid shaped peak of Mt Aspiring (3035m) at the southern end of the Alps. It is the highest peak in the Otagao region and is said to resemble the Matterhorn

The beautiful yet deadly crevasses sculpted on the Tutoko Glacier in Fiordland National Park

Approaching the airfield at Milford Sound, in Fiordland National Park, with the ghostly image of Mitre Peak (1682m) on a dull overcast day

Wrangell National Park, Alaska, USA

Alaska's Wrangell National Park has yet another story to tell and everything about this place usually starts and ends with WOW!

Named after Baron Von Wrangell, the Russian Governor in the days before it was sold to the USA, the park is enormous in size, quality and quantity of unclimbed peaks and glaciers. Covering an area larger than the size of Switzerland it has some of the most amazing examples of glaciers on the planet with The Bagley Ice Field being, for me at any rate, the best anywhere. The largest peaks in the park, Mt Wrangell (4316m) and Mt Sanford (4949m) are both volcanic in nature and are believed to hold about five times the volume of lava that flowed from the dramatic Mt St Helens eruption.

The region owes its magnificent landscape to huge and numerous lava flows from volcanoes that have erupted here over the last 26 million years. This volcanic terrain covers a region of about 10400 square km and stretches eastward from the Copper River Basin through the Wrangell Mountains, into the St. Elias Mountains and the Yukon Territory of Canada.

The geological history of the Alaskan region can be traced back to about 300 million years and the fossil record reveals that a tropical environment existed at the time putting its location in equatorial waters. Like New Zealand, the region probably began as a volcanic arc (i.e. volcanoes that form at subduction zones) along the continental margin of an ancient North American continent. Over the next 100 million years huge outpourings of lava followed by deposition of marine limestone formed the basement rocks of the region.

Over the next 200 million years, plate tectonics gradually transported the region northward, where it eventually docked against western North America about 100 million years ago. Alaska now forms a belt extending from the southern Arctic to the British Columbian border in Canada.

Right

The Bagley Ice Field at 200 km fills a huge region between the Chugach and St. Elias Mountains. The width of the ice field varies between about 6km at its narrowest point to over 24km at its widest. Its depth is on average about 3km, so superlatives are hard to avoid when describing this region of Alaska. The ice field spills seaward branching to form the Malaspina and Bering Glaciers. The two highest peaks in the region are Mt Logan (5959m) and as shown in the image, Mt St Elias (5489m).

Mt St Elias (5489m) looming over the magnificent Bagley Icefield, Alaska

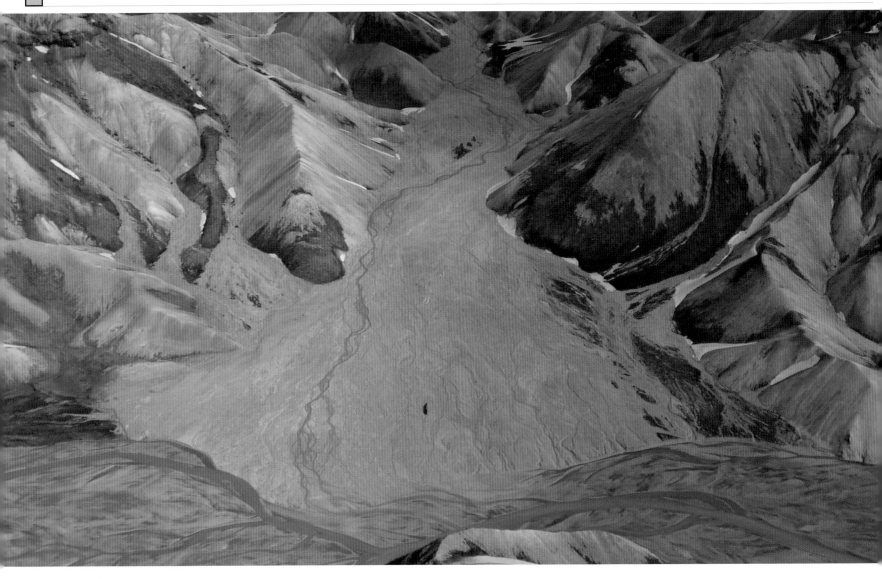

The Torfajökull Volcano located to the south of Landmannalugar is responsible for the rhyolitic lava flows that have shaped this region

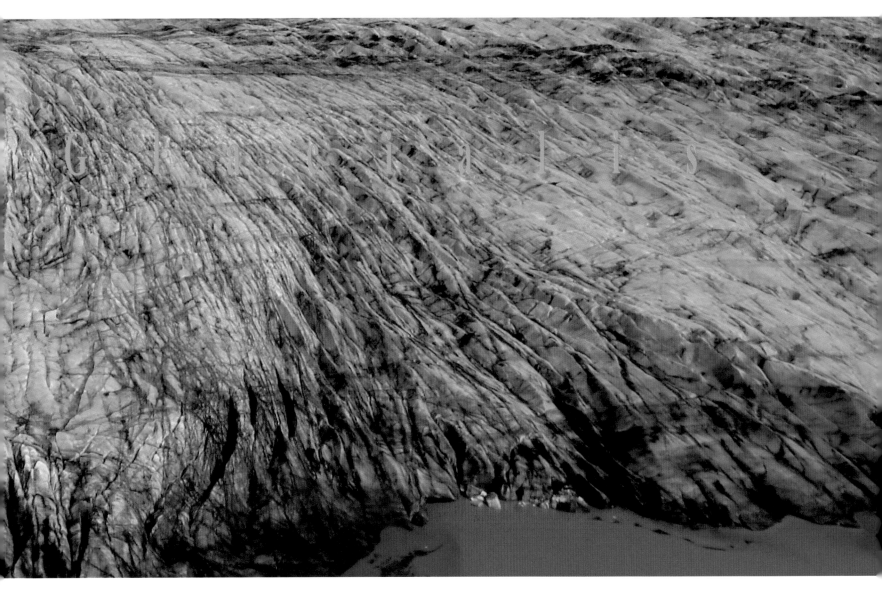

Raw Earth   *Glacialis, Iceland, Skaftafell National Park*

The melting of the Antarctic, Greenland and Icelandic ice sheets and the retreat of glaciers all over the world due to global warming, is constantly in the news these days. These barometers of global climate give us the clearest and most visual indicators that the planet has warmed and records suggest by about 0.6 °C in the last 120 years. The debate about humanity's affect on the climate continues but there is general consensus amongst the scientific community that the industrialization of the planet in the last 120 years has contributed to this temperature rise. The politicians and the industrialists however have reached no such consensus and seem unlikely or, perhaps, unwilling to do so.

So what can we learn by looking at the ice and snow on our planet?

The ice sheets and glaciers are time capsules that tell the story of Earth's atmospheric constituents from the time the snow first started to freeze until the present day. In Antarctica (Vostok Station) and Greenland (GRIP Site) for example, the ice sheets are up to 4000m thick in places and represent snow that first fell there as long ago as 420000 years ago and 100000 years ago respectively.

As the new layers of snow bury the old, the pressure at the lower levels builds up and the density of snow increases. This eventually becomes ice. It is the air that gets trapped between the snowflakes as the snow turns to ice that is the key. Within these tiny bubbles of air is a record of the gases that were present when the snow first fell. By analyzing the isotopic abundances of Carbon Dioxide in these bubbles, a record of the ancient composition of the atmosphere can be obtained.

When data from core ice drilling sites around the world is compared and analyzed it tells a fascinating story of a planet that has undergone quite substantial swings in temperature over the last few hundred thousand years. It shows how something different started to happen about 10000 years ago and which may have contributed to the development of early human civilizations. The Earth was coming out of the last ice age and temperatures started to stabilize at a global average of about 15 °C and have remained so ever since with only very minor fluctuations. It is thought that this globally mild,

temperate and stable climate enabled our ancestors to build the first settlements and develop an agrarian lifestyle, eventually leading to the industrialised society we have today. It is no coincidence that our civilization has flourished during this temperate period.

But the ice cores predict a far more worrying story for the future and one that we have been very slow and reluctant to accept. The stability of the last 10000 years is coming to an end and the world has begun to warm up. This coincides with the advent of the industrial revolution and gathers momentum as we move closer to the present day. There is no doubt, now, that our industrial activities are contributing to the warming of the planet.

As these vast reservoirs of fresh water melt they will cause sea levels to rise, flooding costal regions all over the world. The melting ice also contributes to lowering the temperature of the surrounding oceans which in turn affects something known as the Oceanic Conveyor Belt. This is effectively the Earth's air conditioning system. The colder seas will cause the conveyor to slow down and

eventually stop, resulting in a much cooler climate over large areas of the northern hemisphere. In addition this will also cause drought conditions in the equatorial regions. There is strong evidence, from studies carried out in the North Atlantic, which shows that the conveyor belt has already begun slowing down.

The glacial images that follow are from the Antarctic Peninsula, Alaska, Argentina, Iceland and New Zealand.

Antarctic Peninsula

Some 180 million years ago the super continent of Gondwanaland was being pulled apart by tectonic forces that broke it apart to form what we know today as the continents of India, Australia, South America and Antarctica. Further division occurred to separate Antarctica from all the other landmasses and it then drifted on its plate southwards until it ended up being isolated in the southern ocean at the geographical south of the planet.

The Antarctic is the coldest, windiest and driest place on Earth. It holds 90% of all the ice on the planet and is up to 4775m thick in places. The ice is so heavy that it has depressed the landmass underneath by about 1600m and only 2% of the land is above the ice sheet. It has a surface area of 14 million sq km which doubles in size in the winter. The coldest ever recorded temperature (indeed anywhere) was -89.6 °C in 1983 at Vostok Station.

It was on 26th Jan 1820 that Fabian Von Bellingshausen became the first person to discover this continent which the ancient Greeks had assumed to have existed and had named Terra Australis Incognita (Unknown Southern Continent). It was the Scandinavian Roald Amundsen who on 14th Dec 1911 became the first person to reach the South Pole.

The Antarctic Treaty was signed in 1959 by 12 countries to preserve the pristine beauty of the continent and only allow scientific research which would not impact upon the environment.

Antarctica is fast becoming a 'hot' holiday destination for those seeking something a little different. Maybe it's time for the penguins to start worrying.

These images were taken near Cuverville Island in the Antarctic Peninsula. With nearly 24 hours of daylight and every conceivable shape and size of iceberg, it's only one's imagination that is the limiting factor for any budding photographer. The sea had eaten its way through this single iceberg leaving sections that seemed to fit like two interlocking pieces of a jigsaw puzzle

Further South along the Gerlache Straits, the aptly named Paradise Bay. A few local inhabitants having a party on the ice

Glacialis, Antarctic Peninsula

Glacialis, Antarctic Peninsula   *Raw Earth*

Perito Moreno Glacier, Patagonia, Argentina

Named after explorer Francisco Moreno in the 19th century, this is the largest glacier in Argentina. Like the Franz Josef Glacier in New Zealand, this too is advancing at present. Its terminus is about 5km wide and it has an average height of 60m. At its maximum, the glacier can reach depths of some 700m. Although advancing at a rate of about 2m per day, it loses mass at about the same rate and when it does so the show can be spectacular, as shown in these images.

It is hard to get a sense of just how vast and deep some glacial crevasses can be. In this example from the Tutoko Glacier, the depth was as much as 60m and the width as much as 30-50m

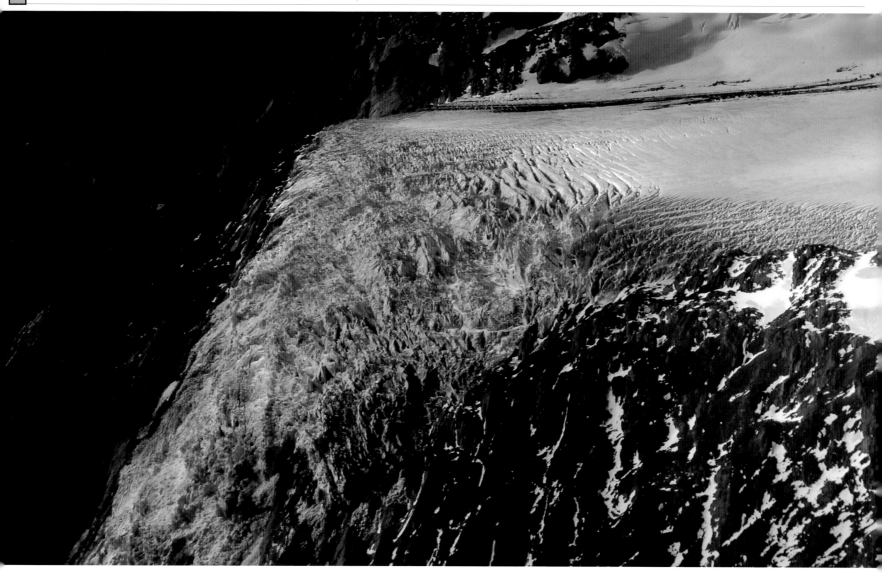

The Franz Josef Glacier is believed to be about 7000 years old and currently extends about 12km from its neve. When the explorer Julian Von Hasst first came across it in 1863, he decided to name the glacier after his emperor but named virtually everything else in the area after himself. Since 1863 the glacier has retreated significantly but has been advancing in the last few years

Glacialis, New Zealand, South Island

Blue Ice? Because the red component (i.e long wavelength) of sunlight is absorbed by ice and the blue component (i.e short wavelength) is transmitted and scattered for longer periods, hence the bluer the ice appears. Glacier hikers such as these are able to witness for themselves the beauty of this blue ice tunnel in the Franz Josef Glacier

Glacialis, New Zealand, South Island   *Raw Earth*   53

The terminus of the Fox Glacier at about 300m deep is presently on the advance. A cave has been carved at its face by subglacial streams

Deep glacial crevasse on the Long Glacier, some are more than 60m deep and highly unstable

Glaciers will pick up and carry along with them anything in their path. The reddish colouration in the image is due to the presence of copper in the rocks. Wrangell National Park, Alaska

Glaciers do not need a slope to flow because it is the accumulation of new snow at its neve that causes the motion, as can be seen in the image. Here at Packsaddle Island the Kennicott Glacier meets the smaller Gates and eventually both merge with the Root Glacier

Aqua

Water is essential to life on our planet, about that there is no doubt. Living organisms have been found that do not require the light and warmth of the sun but none have been found that can exist without water. H_2O covers over 70% of the Earth's surface and has played a fundamental role in its evolution and continues to do so today.

Evidence from zircon crystals, an ubiquitous and virtually indestructible mineral, found in the Jack Hills of Southern Australia suggests that liquid water has been present on our planet from about 200 million years after its formation. It has also been suggested that if liquid water was present, then it would not be unreasonable to suggest that prokaryotic life (a very simple cell without a nucleus and the precursor to Eukaryotic life) may also have been present early on as well. A few scientists believe that they have found the fossils of this basal life form, others remain to be convinced. Of all the planets in our solar system, only Earth has sustained liquid water for virtually all of its history. As we learn more about other planets, we discover that some of them once had liquid water, for example Mars, albeit that it froze up long ago. Furthermore, Europa, one of Jupiter's moons, still retains a liquid ocean encased inside an icy outer shell.

Without water on our planet plate tectonics would never have occurred. It has been found at the regions called subduction zones, where the oceanic crust sinks beneath the continental crust, that liquid water is an essential ingredient. It provides the lubrication that allows the heavier oceanic plate to slide beneath the continental crust and it also lowers the melting point of the subducted rocks. Without liquid water the process of plate tectonics would literally grind to a halt. Thus far, both plate tectonics and the presence of liquid water has only been found on our planet.

Without the watery environment of the primitive oceans, primitive prokaryotic cyanobacteria would not have been able to form stromatolite structures and thereby convert the carbon dioxide into an oxygen rich atmosphere. Over a period of about 2400 million years these tiny life forms were single handedly responsible for oxygenating the Earth and thereby enabling more complex life to evolve, about 560 million years ago in a period known as the Cambrian Explosion.

New technology has allowed us in the last few decades to venture to the bottom of the ocean floor, making some amazing discoveries in the process. We have found a crack running virtually all around the planet from where new ocean floor is being created by underwater volcanoes. In addition, we have found regions where ocean floor sinks beneath continents. Smokers (huge chimneys belching out a broth of super heated water and minerals) have been discovered on the seabed and amazingly an abundance of life forms have been found to exist in this harsh environment. One theory of how life on Earth began suggests that the first primitive life evolved around these smokers. They used the mineral rich environment as an abundant food source to thrive, far away from the harsh environment at the surface where the Sun's cosmic radiation destroyed any organic activity. We have found canyons that plunge nearly 11000m below sea level, revealing a cacophony of life forms that stretch the imagination in their variety and abundance. Even the mud beneath the ocean floor is revealing its secrets of times past when temperatures where much hotter. Indeed, the Earth may even at one time have been a giant ball of ice. With these discoveries we have come to learn of past catastrophic events that have driven nearly all life on Earth to extinction at various times in its history.

Water also formed the basis of early human civilization. Around 10000 years ago as the last ice age was coming to an end and the ice sheets retreated, human civilization was beginning to evolve from a hunter gatherer lifestyle and establish the first small settlements of an agrarian existence. The Sumerians, the Indus Valley Civilization, the Egyptians, the early Chinese and the Mesoamericans all based their first cities on or around major sources of water, as far back as 7000 years ago. Cultures based on agriculture appeared independently of one another in and around river valleys such as the Tigris, Euphrates, Nile, Indus and Yellow in China. The access to and the ownership of strategic water sources have been the root of many conflicts throughout our history and attests to the fundamental importance of this inert, yet vital liquid.

The photographs that follow encompass some of the most aesthetically pleasing images of an aquatic Earth. Ranging from beautiful turquoise-blue lakes, complex networks of braided rivers, gentle flowing glacial streams, to waterfalls carved out over volcanic landscapes.

The mighty Godley River with the heads of the Tasman and Murchison Glaciers to the left and the Sibald Range to the right

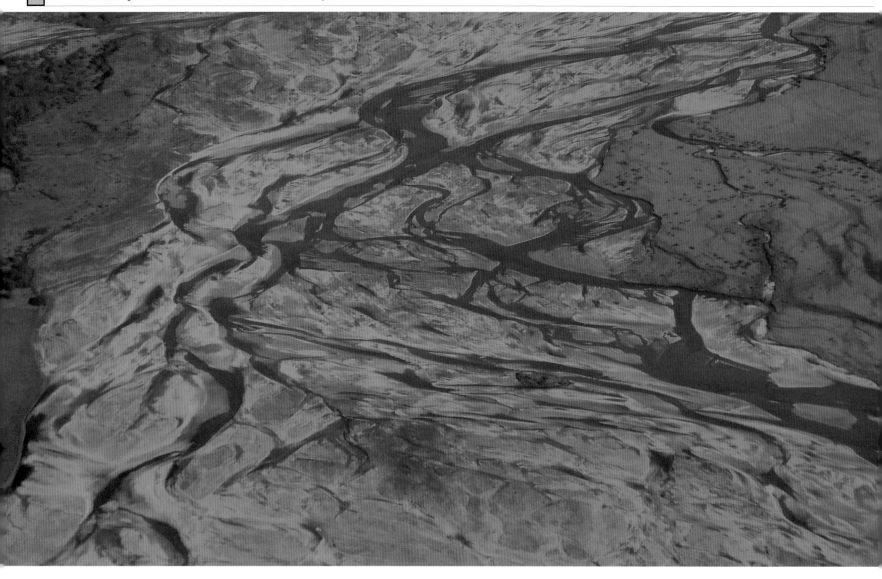

In November 1996 the Grimsvötn Volcano erupted beneath the huge Vatnajökull ice cap causing a massive jökulhlaup, or glacial burst. About 5 miles of the nearby Highway 1 was washed away and the aftermath was the largest sandur (glaciofuvial deposits formed by braided river systems) in Iceland. Now known as Skeiðarársandur

Raw Earth   *Aqua, Iceland, Skeiðarársandur*

Both images below show the effects of glaciation at The Chasm, near Milford Sound. Some of these boulders could easily match the size of a house and all have been transported to their present location as glacial moraine

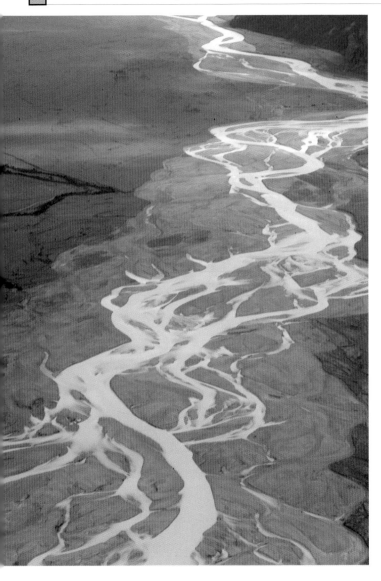

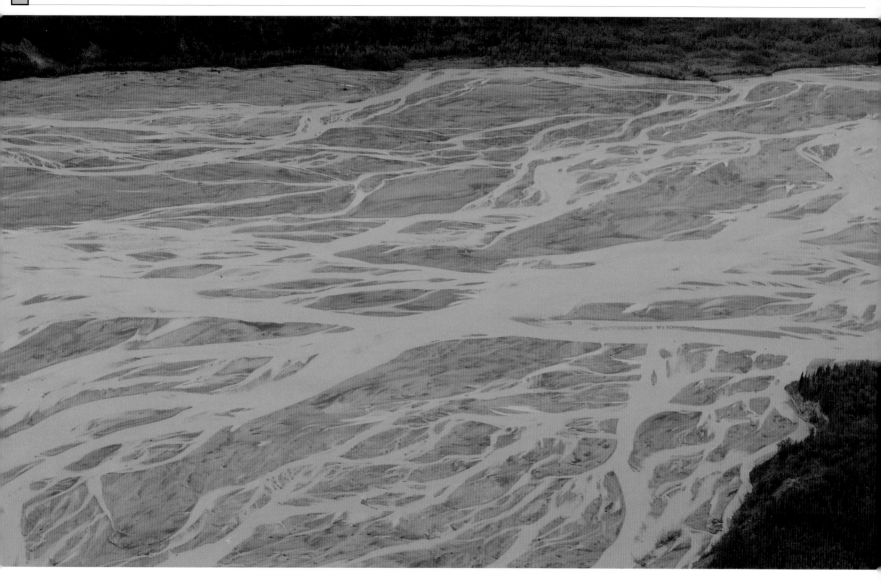

The entrance to Milford Sound from the Tasman Sea, Fiordland National Park. At a length of 16km it is home to Mitre Peak and has some of the most stunning landscape in New Zealand. Sheer granite cliffs soar directly from the sea to heights of 1692m and the water is alive with an abundance of marine life

Milford Sound from above Mitre Peak. The sightseeing ship near the centre of the image gives an idea of the scale of this Fiord

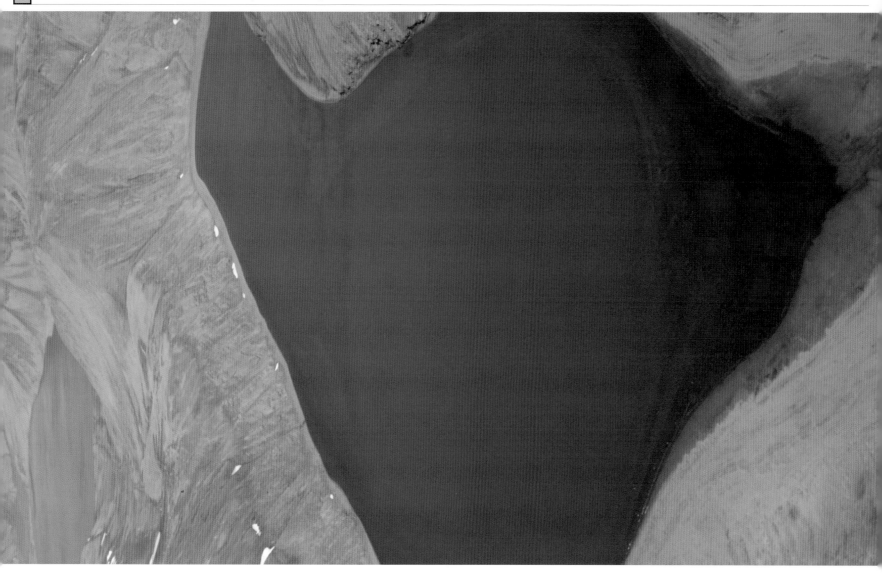

The tranquility of Lake Tekapo with Aoraki/Mt Cook National Park in the distance. The lake is over 120 metres deep and has an average temperature of 7 °C

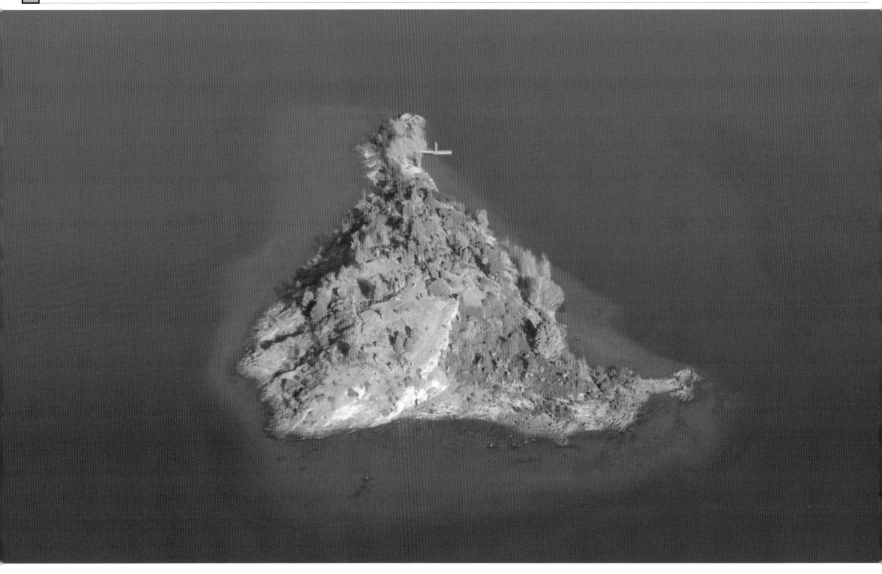

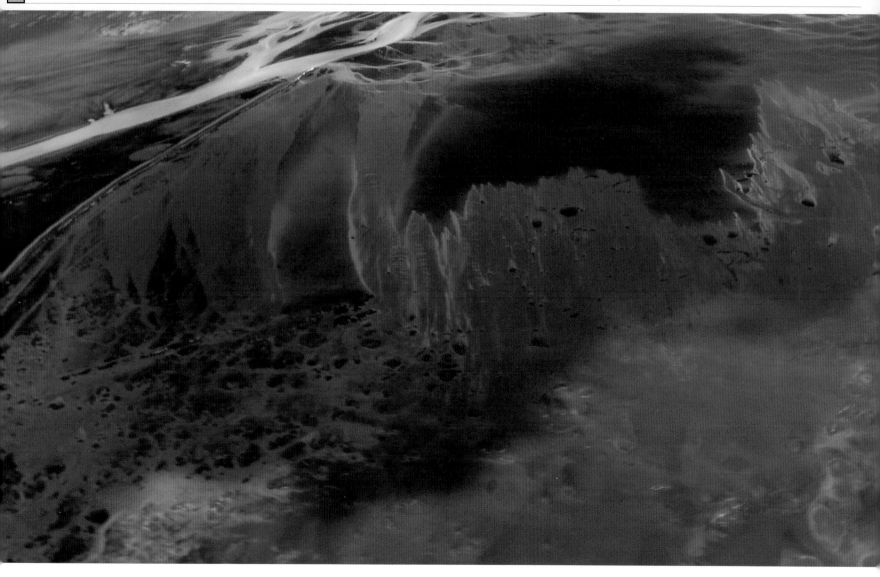

Aqua, Iceland, South Coast   **Raw Earth**

Inferno

The history of the Earth is littered with cataclysmic events, the magnitude of which we can only begin to imagine. Most of these have been of a volcanic nature and their effects have often changed the course of Earth history. The roots of volcanism go all the way back to the very creation of our planet some 4560 million years ago and what we see today, with volcanoes all around the globe, is that the story is still unfolding.

The Earth and indeed all planets are believed to have formed by the gravitational accretion of tiny dust and ice particles over many hundreds of million of years. As these tiny particles coalesced they formed bigger conglomerates of matter which in turn attracted even more matter through their mutual gravitation. This ultimately formed a proto-planet. At the center, or core, the pressure would have gradually increased as the accumulated mass grew and in turn the internal temperature would also have risen. In the case of our Earth, external temperatures reached 1200 °C and all the iron, everywhere on the planet, melted. Because it was heavier than all the other elements, the iron sank to the centre. Hence it is believed that

our planet's core is primarily a solid single ball, maybe even a single iron crystal. Surrounding this is a sea of liquid iron at temperatures in excess of 5500 °C and pressures of around 1-3 million atmospheres. Recent studies suggest for the Earth to have maintained its heat source for so long a period of time, that there must also be radioactive Uranium present within the core.

In very simple terms, one could say that the Earth is just trying to release all the thermodynamic energy amassed during its creation and reach a state of equilibrium with its surroundings.

It was the English scientist Lord Rayleigh who first put forward the idea that if there was such a vast source of heat at the centre of the Earth, then maybe it was convecting its heat outwards? This idea was, later in the 20th century, to be a key component in the theory of plate tectonics and led to a fuller understanding of the dynamics of the Earth. Consequently, scientists were able to put together a theory that explained why tectonic plates move as they do. They also began to take on board what happens at the oceanic ridges at the bottom of

the sea floor, and what happens at subduction zones. The theory also resolved the mystery of how mountain building and volcanism fits into the picture.

Volcanism, was revealed to be the final surface expression of the enormous amounts of molten material stored within the Earth, and its continents had been formed over millions of years of such volcanism. The mystery of why so much volcanic activity takes place along the boundary of where the Pacific Ocean meets the continents was solved. This was attributed to vast slabs of the ocean floor subducting underneath the North American, Cocos, Nazca, Antarctic, Australian, Eurasian and Philippine plates. The origins of the oceans were also partly attributable to outgassing of the heat from within the planet. The images of Mt Yasur in Vanuatu are a direct manifestation of such activity.

The story of Iceland, as we shall see later, is also one of extreme volcanic activity. Deep below the Earth's surface a new entity called a Mantle Plume (a Hot Spot) was discovered. It was later found that these plumes were also responsible not only for the

formation of the Hawaiian Islands, but also vast areas of India (known as the Deccan Traps) and furthermore, the activity of such plumes may have contributed to the causes of the extinction of the dinosaurs. We know that a vast meteorite hit the Earth some 65 million years ago. This caused immense damage and destruction to an area in the Yucatan Peninsula (present day Mexico). However, what is not so commonly known, is that at about the same time, on the other side of the planet (in what is now India) a plume was ejecting truly immense quantities of magma over a very long period of time. This outpouring of magma and the associated release of noxious gases into the atmosphere, coupled with the cataclysmic events on the other side of the planet, inflicted a double whammy upon the dinosaurs from which they had no chance of surviving.

The North Island of New Zealand also owes its existence to volcanic activity generated by the subduction of the Pacific plate beneath the Australian plate and giving rise to areas such as Wai-O-Tapu and Whakarewarewa thermal regions.

Iceland

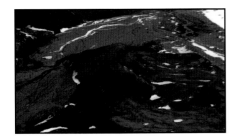

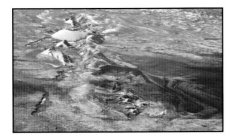

There is, perhaps, no better example of volcanic activity anywhere on the planet than on Iceland. This land is also one of extreme geothermal activity and hence it is often called the land of fire and ice.

Located just below the Arctic circle between 63°16`-66°30`N and 13°51`-24°13`W Iceland has the dubious privilege of sitting above a point where two of Earth's massive tectonic plates are tearing apart. If that were not enough, below these plates is a mantle plume, a huge reservoir of molten material rising directly from the Earth's core. It is thought that it was the action of this mantle plume pushing through the crust and causing an enormous split that formed the Mid Atlantic Ridge, the Atlantic Ocean and in the process also resulted in the formation of Iceland, about 25 million years ago. It is the only place on Earth where one can see the tectonic plates above the surface and physically walk between them.

The rocks here are the youngest anywhere on the planet, with the oldest surface rocks being no more than 14-16 million years old. Contrast that with its neighbour, Greenland, where we find the oldest rocks at about 4000 million years.

There are volcanoes and fissures in every direction of all sizes and types but for me, the most fascinating is where fire meets ice, as in the Grimsvötn volcano. In the southeast region we find the Vatnajökull Icecap, it's the large white blob on the map, and directly below it sits Grimsvötn. It is believed that this volcano is the surface expression of the mantle plume which originally formed Iceland. When it erupted in 1996, it sent over 50000 cubic meters per second of melt water mud and anything it picked up, seaward in a huge torrent that lasted over 24 hours.

The geological activity in Iceland has also had global repercussions as was the case with the Laki eruptions of 1783 and the Eldgjá eruptions of 934-40. It is now known that the Laki eruption caused global average temperatures to fall by about 1.3°C and also that the effects were felt throughout mainland Europe.

Inferno, Iceland, Vatnajökull region

'Desolation Row': On the 1st of June 1783 the inhabitants of the southern coastal regions felt strong earthquakes from Myrdalur to Oræfi. By 8th June dark volcanic clouds spread across the entire region. The great Laki Eruption had commenced. Over the next 9 months a 27km long fissure opened up and walls of lava over 1000m high filled the landscape

The spectacular and destructive Laki fissure erupted along 27km, through 140 active vents and over ten episodes lasting 9 months. Its column reached a height of 10km and stretched all the way to the European mainland and the Arctic

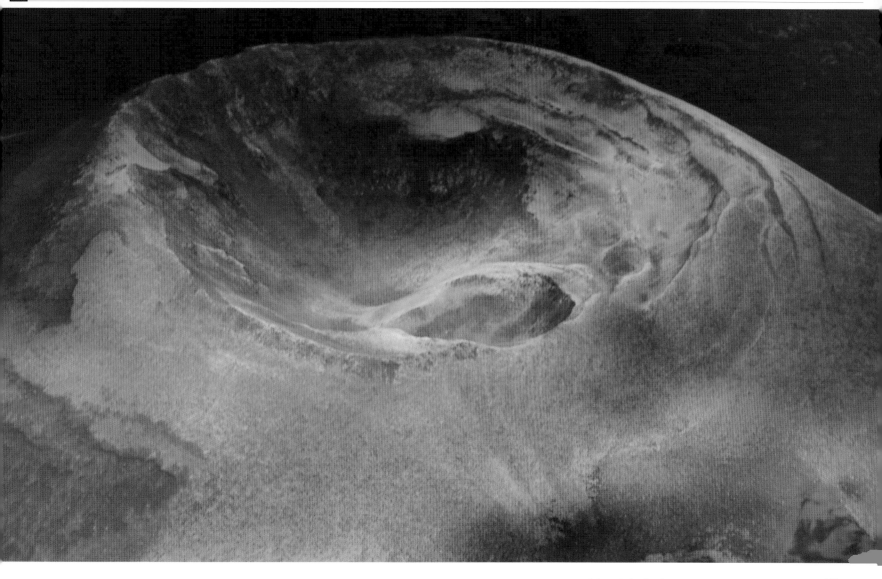

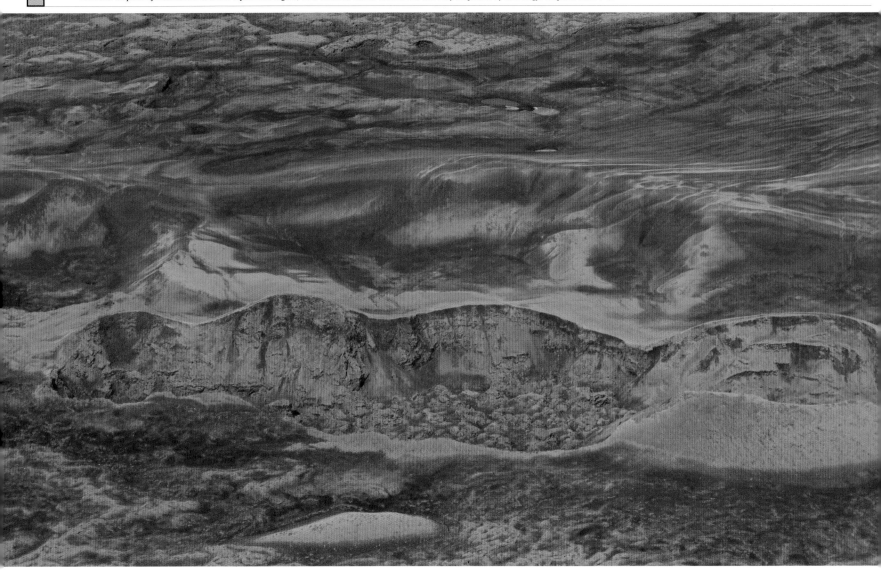

The Geysir geothermal field is a major tourist attraction and its reputation is such that all hot springs throughout the world are thus known as geysers. Unfortunately the original Geysir has had its day and it is now up to Strokkur, an adjoining hot spring, to impress the visitors. It can reach heights of up to 100m on rare occasions

Pingvellir National Park. This image clearly shows a section of the mid Atlantic Ridge which passes through Iceland. To the left one can see the North American plate and to the right the Eurasian. Pingvellir is located at the western end of the rift which extends from the mountains in the northeast down to Pingvallavatn

Located in the Pacific Ocean about 3 hours flying time from Sydney, AU, sits Vanuatu, an archipelago of 83 islands. On the remote island of Tanna one finds a unique combination of pristine beaches and one of the most accessible volcanoes in the world, Mt Yasur. Even though it is only 360m above sea level it's still an adventure getting to the summit across miles of black ash plains and virtually non existent roads that have been washed away by heavy rains. Once atop the summit, Mt Yasur rewards you for your efforts by putting on an outstanding display of fireworks. Most people, including the writer, are awestruck at just how close one can get to the fiery cauldron of molten rock. Then as if to really knock you of your feet, it lets out an almighty boom that reverberates all around the mountain and usually has the effect of sending most people racing back down the slopes. If you were brave enough to stick around you would witness the awesome power of the fountains of molten rock that are sent hurtling repeatedly skywards. Truly an awe inspiring sight!

At only 360m above sea level Mt Yasur is an easy climb but beware of the rain of black ash, ejecting about every ten minutes. Even on a rainy day there's something to see as vast clouds of smoke and ash are blown out

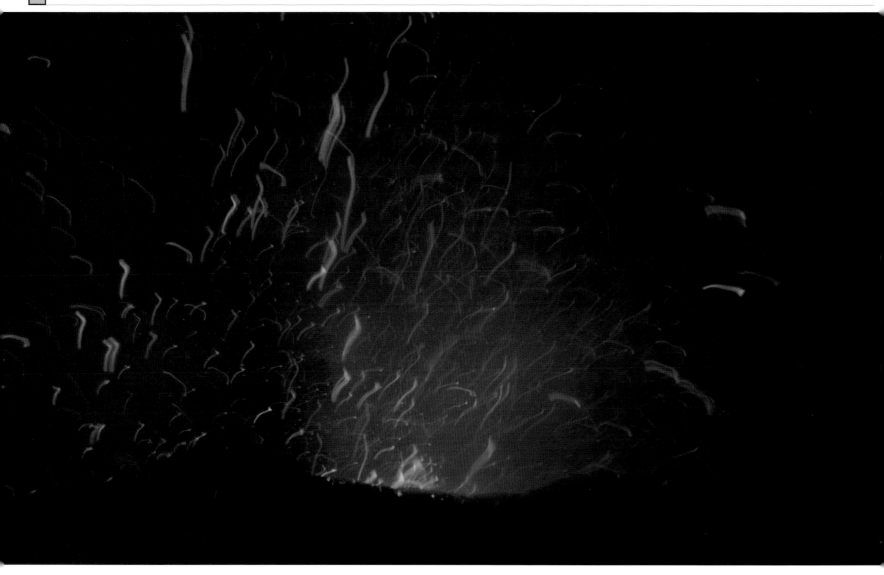

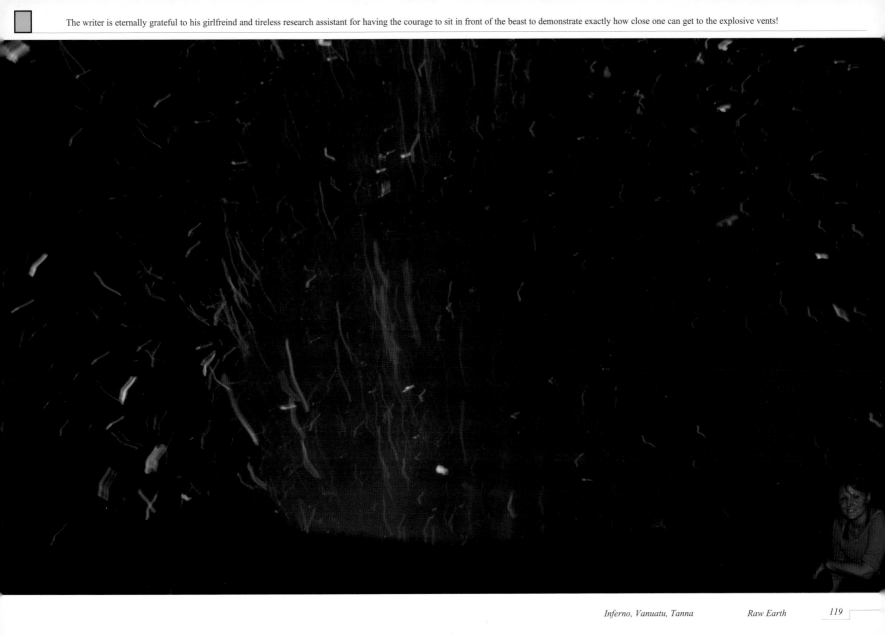

North Island, New Zealand

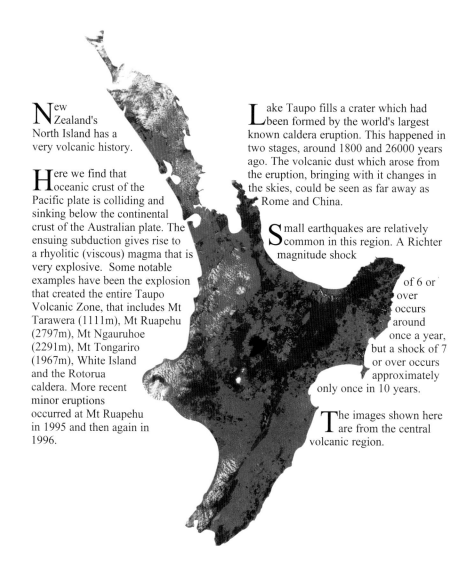

New Zealand's North Island has a very volcanic history.

Here we find that oceanic crust of the Pacific plate is colliding and sinking below the continental crust of the Australian plate. The ensuing subduction gives rise to a rhyolitic (viscous) magma that is very explosive. Some notable examples have been the explosion that created the entire Taupo Volcanic Zone, that includes Mt Tarawera (1111m), Mt Ruapehu (2797m), Mt Ngauruhoe (2291m), Mt Tongariro (1967m), White Island and the Rotorua caldera. More recent minor eruptions occurred at Mt Ruapehu in 1995 and then again in 1996.

Lake Taupo fills a crater which had been formed by the world's largest known caldera eruption. This happened in two stages, around 1800 and 26000 years ago. The volcanic dust which arose from the eruption, bringing with it changes in the skies, could be seen as far away as Rome and China.

Small earthquakes are relatively common in this region. A Richter magnitude shock of 6 or over occurs around once a year, but a shock of 7 or over occurs approximately only once in 10 years.

The images shown here are from the central volcanic region.

Inferno, New Zealand, North Island   *Raw Earth*

The Wai-O-Tapu thermal area is associated with volcanic activity dating back to 160,000 years ago and is located on the edge of the huge volcanic caldera known as Lake Taupo. One of the largest features is the Champagne Pool measuring 65m in diameter and 62m deep. The pool formed about 700 years ago and the distinctive colouring is due to deposits of gold, silver, mercury, sulphur, arsenic, thallium and antimony at the rim of the pool

References

The Rise and Fall of The Southern Alps, Glen Coates and Geoffery Cox

World History A New Perspective, Clive Ponting

Iceland, Thor Thordarson and Armann Hoskuldsson

New Scientist, numerous articles and issues relating to geophysics, Earth Sciences and geology over the last 20 years

Scientific American, numerous articles and issues relating to geophysics, Earth Sciences and geology over the last 20 years

National Geographic, numerous articles and issues relating to geology and Earth Sciences from 2004-present

Antarctica The Lost Continent, Kim Heacox (NationalGeographic)

Antartica Expedition Guide, Margaret Abbott

Earth -The Evolution of a Habitable World, Jonathan I Lunine

Picture Journey in Alaska's Wrangell-St Elias America's Largest National Park, George Herben

Iceland, Cathy Harlow

Websites

All latitude and longitude measurements are from Google Earth.

All satellite images of the Earth, Alaska, Antarctica, Argentina, Iceland, New Zealand and Vanuatu are with kind permission of:

http://visibleearth.nasa.gov/

Wrangell & St Elias National Park

http://www.nps.gov/wrst/geology.htm
http://gorp.away.com/gorp/resource/us_national_park
/ak/geo_wran.htm

Pronunciation of Icelandic letters

á as used in *house*
æ as used in *eye*
é as used in *yet*
ó as used in *sold*
ö as used in *turn*
∂ as used in ***that***

Index

Index